*Guest Curators*

Laurie Adelson
Bruce Takami

# WEAVING TRADITIONS OF HIGHLAND BOLIVIA

December 19, 1978 to
February 4, 1979

Craft and Folk Art Museum,
Los Angeles

# CONTENTS

(above) *An Uru woman gathering reeds from the Rio Desaguadero.* (opposite) *Detail of no. 74, a mantilla (ceremonial cloth) from the Dept. of La Paz. The designs are typical of the Lake Titicaca region.*

© Laurie Adelson and Bruce Takami
Library of Congress Catalog Card # 78-73710

## PREFACE

As with every facet of art, first comes the excitement of discovery; after the excitement comes intellectual curiosity, and for most of us, passion is the culmination of the adventure. Handmade fibers which are spun, dyed, woven, and formed into sensual, tactile, aesthetic objects do this to me.

Laurie Adelson and Bruce Takami have been taking me through the whole process with their collection of Bolivian textiles and costumes. I was aware of the beauty of Bolivian textiles, but now I know they must be the most exquisitely spun and handwoven objects anywhere. Our curators have spent several years traveling on foot through the Bolivian Andes. They have learned to speak the Indian Quechua language, and in so doing have learned of the traditional reverence of the Bolivians for their textile traditions. This reverence is communicated to us through our magnificent exhibition of their collection, as well as the heretofore unwritten information in the text of the catalogue.

Thank you, Laurie and Bruce, for this splendid experience.

*EDITH WYLE*

Ever since we first became involved with Bolivian textiles, it has been our desire to share them with other people. We are indebted to Edith Wyle whose enthusiasm and openness has made this exhibition possible.

In addition, we would like to thank the following people for their help:
Paul and Elaine Adelson
Nancy Bloch
Mary Jane Leland
Mary Moser
The Museum of Cultural History,
    University of California, Los Angeles
Charles and Anita Rosenblum
Hugo Danial Ruíz, Director del Museo
    Nacional de Etnografía y Folklore
William Siegal and Karen Abendroth
Arthur Tracht
Roger Yorke
The entire staff of the
    Craft and Folk Art Museum

We would especially like to thank Dr. Giles W. Mead for securing funds for this project and for his help and encouragement on many levels.

*LAURIE A. ADELSON*
*BRUCE C. TAKAMI*

The textile tradition of highland Bolivia is a rich and highly developed art with roots reaching back to pre-Colombian times. Yet this remarkable tradition has gone largely unrecognized outside of the Bolivian rural regions where weaving is still the most important form of creative expression.

Originally, textile production arose out of the simple need for clothing. Gradually, complicated techniques and designs evolved and cloth became a significant social element in the lives of the Andean peoples. Today in Bolivia, weaving is a well-respected, non-commercial art; in most regions cloth continues to play a major role in the lives of the Indians. All members of the family are involved in textile production. The simple indigenous loom and drop spindle are still used to produce a wide variety of weavings ranging from plain, utilitarian textiles for daily use, to highly sophisticated and refined pieces of extraordinary quality for use in ceremonies and festivals. When not tending animals, farming, or doing other daily chores, most people are engaged in weaving-related activities. Although in some respects costume has changed over the years, the complex weaving techniques of the past are very much alive.

Recent years have brought many changes to Bolivia and modernization reaches even to remote highland areas. The influence of technology can already be seen as the rural people begin to wear machine-made rather than handmade clothes. Many aspects of the ancient art are already lost. Little natural dyeing is done and the skill of extremely fine spinning is preserved in only a few areas. Industrial wool and synthetics sometimes appear in modern textiles.

Due to the breakdown of traditional values, the Indians themselves have forgotten much of the meaning that cloth once had. Few people now understand the significance of the symbols they weave and little research has been done on native Bolivian weaving. Consequently, there is limited documentation and one must rely largely on what information can be gathered today by personal contact. Unfortunately, as the older generation dies out, much information is lost. It is hoped, however, that recent interest in Bolivian weaving will stimulate further research, and that the weavers will receive the recognition they deserve.

# INTRODUCTION

Most of the Indians of highland Bolivia belong to two distinct groups of people: The Aymaras, the pre-Incan inhabitants of Bolivia, living mainly on the *altiplano*, or high plain, at an altitude of about 12,500 feet (3812 meters), and the Quechuas, the Indians who adopted the official language of the Incas and who live in the mountain valleys of the Cordillera Real. Two other groups, the Urus near the Desaguadero River and the Chipayas on the southern end of the Bolivian altiplano, are also highland dwellers but now exist only in small numbers. Each of these groups has its own distinct cultural traditions including language and dress.

## AYMARAS

The Aymaras (previously called *Collas*)[1] were a large and powerful group long before their conquest by the Incas which began in the 11th century A.D. At that time, the Aymaras were divided into a number of separate states covering an extensive area of what is now highland Bolivia and southern Peru, reaching all the way to the Pacific coast and extending as far north as present-day Lima.[2] Examples of textiles from that period show that these people were excellent weavers who used many diverse and complex weaving techniques.

The Aymaras strongly resisted Incan incursion into their territory and it took the Incas four centuries to totally conquer them. Even then, the Aymaras paid tribute, but refused to accept the official language (Quechua) or Incan customs. At the same time, the Incas encouraged their subjects to maintain their traditional dress and it is therefore likely that Aymara weaving and costume changed little during Incan domination.

Although the advent of the Spanish greatly influenced native textiles, the many fine weavings which have survived from the beginning of the Republic (1825) and onward indicate that the traditional respect for weaving was never lost. Aymaras still maintain the custom of handing down old matrimonial and ceremonial garments from generation to generation. Among these textiles are some of the best examples of post-Colonial weaving. Often made from finely spun alpaca, these pieces demonstrate the delicate use of design and natural dyes which the Aymaras incorporated into their beautiful and often highly sophisticated fabrics.

## QUECHUAS

Quechua, the official language of the Incas, was imposed on all peoples under the Inca realm. Many Aymaras resisted the lingual change but those who accepted the State language became known as Quechuas. Today the Quechuas comprise the majority of the Bolivian highlanders. It is interesting to note that the language is still spreading.

During the Inca Empre, textiles were of utmost importance and much time and energy were devoted to them. While all people wove, special women were cloistered in convents and their chief occupation was weaving the fine clothes of the nobles, special sacrificial pieces, and

(opposite) *A woman from the Bolívar region: The Indians of this area were originally Aymara but now speak Quechua.*

clothing for the army. Textiles played a major role at all significant occasions including puberty rites, marriage, and particularly death, as indicated by the great quantities of cloth found at burial sites. So important was cloth that some textiles even had their own deity, *Aksu-mama*, to whom weavings were sacrificed each year. The finest textiles were called *cumbi*, and large quantities were burned annually in sacrifice to the sun. Cloth was the most highly valued gift and a primary source of revenue for the State.

## URUS AND CHIPAYAS

The Urus and the Chipayas are the only other distinct groups that live on the Bolivian altiplano. Both once spoke dialects of *Puquina*, a language unconnected to Aymara and Quechua. However, Aymara and Spanish have practically replaced *Puquina*.

The Urus are thought to be the earliest inhabitants of the altiplano. They themselves claim to be the oldest race in the world, pre-dating the sun. The Urus once inhabited many of the islands of Lake Titicaca but they are now mainly confined to a few islands and a small area on the banks of the Rio Desaguadero. Having virtually no land to cultivate, the Urus subsist mainly on fish and waterfowl from the river. They generally fish at night, using *balsas*, boats made from *totora* reed, and hunt with bolas called *tschonis* which they fling at ducks to entangle them.

(opposite) *A man from the Bolívar region, playing* zampoñas *(pan pipes) at the* Tinku *festival.* (above) *An Ayamara woman and child from the Leque region.*

Although little remains of the traditional costume of the Urus, they still wear the *ira (Puquina)*, a long tunic that protects them from the damp cold when they fish at night.

The Chipayas live on the isolated salt flats west of Lake Coipasa. They consider themselves to be the last survivors of the *chullpa* people who were supposedly exterminated by the sun. Chipaya traditions are better preserved than those of the Urus, perhaps due to their remote location. They continue to live in round, thatched huts as their ancestors did. The women plait their hair in many tiny braids and the *ira* is still worn.

## DEVELOPMENT OF WEAVING AND DRESS

The heddle loom and other weaving implements used by present-day Bolivian weavers were developed by their ancestors over 3000 years ago. So creative were these people that before the first century A.D., they had developed most of the weaving techniques which were eventually to be used all over Peru and Bolivia. The few pre-Colombian highland textiles that have survived indicate that a rich and impressive weaving tradition was already flourishing in the mountains well over 1000 years ago. By the time the Spaniards arrived in the 16th century, both coastal and highland weaving were at such a high point that the conquistadors were astounded by the richness and beauty of Incan clothing.

The influence of the Spanish on weaving and costume soon began to show. Sheep, brought from Europe, provided wool as a new fiber and the treadle loom was introduced. Certain aspects of Spanish dress, such as pants and European-type hats, were adopted by the Indians, and the Spanish soon began to regulate native dress. The Indians were prohibited from dressing like Europeans and a whole series of charters and laws were passed declaring that natives must not wear luxurious clothing.

In 1780, the Aymaras of Bolivia (then Alto Perú) and the Quechuas under Tupac Amaru, led a strong insurrection against the Colonial government. The Indians were defeated but the government decided that in order to prevent further uprisings they must erase all signs of differentiation between the natives and the colonialists. The Indians were therefore prohibited from wearing their regional clothes and were ordered to adopt the costume of the Spanish peasant.

In the highlands and less accessible regions, the Indians were able to preserve their customs to a certain extent. The remoteness of many weaving communities has enabled Bolivians to maintain a tradition of high quality warp-patterned weaving. While Spanish elements still make up a major part of the Bolivian Indians' clothing, indigenous garments are worn along with them to form a costume that is distinctly Andean.

*Two Sixteenth Century drawings by Felipe Guamán Poma de Ayala: (below) An Inca woman working at a backstrap loom. This type of loom is still used by Bolivian weavers; (opposite) An Inca queen. She is wearing an* aksu *(tunic-like dress), a* lliclla *(mantle), a* p'anta *(headcloth), and a* chumpi *(belt). The* lliclla *is fastened with a* topo *(pin). The modern Bolivian costume was derived by combining these elements of dress with some Spanish garments.*

# LASEGVNDA COIA
# CHINBOVRMA

Reyno barta hatuncolla

chinbo

## FIBERS

Before the arrival of the Spanish, camelids (alpaca, llama and vicuña) were the primary sources for weaving materials in Bolivia. Alpaca was the preferred fiber and it is still highly valued. When finely spun and woven, it yields a shiny, silky fabric.

Llama hair is coarser and stronger than alpaca and is therefore generally chosen for utilitarian textiles such as *costales* (storage sacks). The rarest and most highly prized fiber comes from the wild vicuña. In Incan times only the head Inca himself could bestow the right to wear vicuña. Since the Spanish conquest, indiscriminate killing of the animal has caused it to become an endangered species so that vicuña hunting is now prohibited.

Sheep's wool, introduced by the Spanish, is now the most available and commonly used material although it yields a rather rough fabric unless much care is taken in shearing and sorting the wool. By selecting fibers from different parts of the animal's body, various qualities of yarn may be spun. The fibers from around the neck are the finest and those toward the back are the coarsest. The weaver may pick superior fibers for her important textiles and coarser ones for utilitarian pieces.

Cotton is native to South America but it is not often used in the highlands. It is rarely handspun and its use is limited to certain regions and to particular types of weavings. In Tarabuco, for example, it is woven along with wool, but only in the patterned areas of the pieces. Obviously, in the cold climates of Bolivia, warmer materials are preferred.

Recently, weavers have begun using machine-spun yarns, both natural and synthetic. These industrial yarns simplify the weaving process inasmuch as the initial spinning and dyeing are already done. Furthermore, there is a great deal of prestige in being able to purchase industrial products.

## SPINNING

Bolivian spinners have produced some of the most finely spun sheep and camelid yarns in the world using only a simple drop spindle. The wool goes through three spinning processes: It is initially spun on a small spindle to obtain a single strand from the raw wool. Next, a larger spindle is used to make a two-ply yarn. After dyeing, the yarn is given a third spinning to produce a crepe twist, a spin so tight that the yarn, when not under tension, twists back on itself. This "overspin" is an important feature of Bolivian yarns, giving it great strength, elasticity, and a hard, smooth surface. These qualities aid the weaver and the result is a fine, yet durable fabric.

Bolivians sometimes make deliberate use of S- and Z-twisted (clockwise and counterclockwise) yarns in their fabrics. Often, in a predominantly S-twisted fabric, one finds stripes or single warp threads of alternating S- and Z-twisted yarns. Z-twisted threads are called *lloq'e* and are said to bring good luck and ward off evil.

**THE WEAVING PROCESS**

(opposite) *A girl from Yanahuaya weaving on a horizontal ground loom.*

(right) *A man and woman selling aniline dyes at the market in Jesús de Machaca, Dept. of La Paz.* (opposite) *Balls of handspun yarn ready for dyeing and weaving.*

Not only do they add a lovely subtle effect to the weavings, but also, when near the edges of fabrics, they help prevent the corners from curling.

## DYEING

Bolivian textiles were once dyed with a remarkable variety of natural materials which yielded a wide range of beautiful colors. The art of dyeing was a time-consuming and sophisticated process that involved an intimate understanding of plants, their parts and life cycles. According to Daniel W. Gade, "The Quechua language has an elaborate terminology for all aspects of the dyeing process and we may suppose that in past times it was a very important activity."[3]

*Cochineal,* an insect that lives on the leaves of the nopal cactus, made a very popular dye, producing shades from pale pink to a deep carmine and possibly even purple. Red dye was extracted from the seeds of a cactus called *airampu. Nogal* (walnut) is still used today to obtain golds and browns. Girault names *anil (Indigofera sp.,* Leguminosae) for blue, *ayapana (Eupatorium ayapana,* Composacae) for ultramarine, and *sauco (Sambucus nigra,* Caprilacae) whose fruit yielded a violet color. Some natural dyes were brought from Europe by the Spaniards and many other dyes were available from the lichens and plants of Bolivia.[4] Mordants, materials which aid in the binding of dyes, also alter colors, adding even more variation. In Bolivia, alum is a traditional

mordant. Lime may be used and urine is very common as well.

Since the importation of aniline dyes from Europe began in the latter part of the 19th century, natural dyeing has been steadily on the decline. Today, little of the ancient art is known. Aniline dyes are inexpensive, readily available, require little time to prepare, and thus are very popular. Though not as subtle as traditional dyes, anilines are effectively used by artisans to create lovely and dramatic color combinations.

## WEAVING

Girls usually begin learning to weave before puberty. Most indigenous textiles are woven by women on the traditional heddle loom. The loom is set up outside of the house and may be positioned either horizontally, with the loom bars lashed to stakes in the ground, or obliquely, leaning against a wall with the loom bars tied to two perpendicular poles. A backstrap loom is also sometimes used.

Most weaving occurs during the winter season, after the harvest and before the next year's planting. The women spend

many of their daylight hours at the loom, simultaneously attending to the children and other daily chores. A complex piece with a large patterned area may take several months to complete. Because of the time involved in weaving, these fabrics are made to last many years.

An important feature of indigenous Bolivian textiles is that they have four selvedges.[5] This is accomplished by using a continuous warp which is woven entirely from one end to the other. Since these textiles are warp patterned, the basic layout is determined during the warping process. In the areas where patterning is desired, two or more colors are warped together so that the weaver may "pick up" the color she needs to create the designs. The second color falls to the other side, resulting in a totally reversible cloth.[6] The design motifs are identical on both sides; only the colors change. In a few regions, long supplementary warp floats are used, producing pieces which have design only on one side.

Techniques and embellishments vary considerably according to the tradition of each region. Different structures are achieved, depending on how the loom is warped and the way in which the weft threads are inserted during weaving. A resist dye technique called *watado* (*ikat*), may also be used for patterning. The edges of fabrics are often protected with a woven tubing called *ribete*. Certain pieces are adorned with tassels or beading depending on local custom.[7]

Yardage, called *bayeta*, is woven in most regions on a European-style treadle loom.

Usually woven by men, *bayeta* is then tailored into garments such as shirts, pants and dresses. Many men weave very bright plaids for their vests, jackets and sashes. A balanced plain weave is commonly used but occasionally twills may be woven.

In the central highlands men make belts for their wives or girlfriends on a lap loom called a *cañar*. A type of weft wrapping is employed with thick warp threads resulting in a stiff but durable belt.

(left) *A woman from the Calcha region plying yarn with a drop spindle.* (below) *An oblique loom from the Macha region. Above the woven design area many small string heddles can be seen.*

## COSTUME

The Quechuas and the Aymaras share many elements of costume, reflecting a mixture of pre-Colombian tradition with Spanish influence. Some pieces of the man's costume in particular are non-Andean in origin and are woven on a European-type treadle loom. These include the *pantalones* (pants), *almillia* or *camisa* (shirt), *chaleco* (vest), *chaqueta* (jacket), and *chalina* (sash). Only two elements of male pre-Hispanic dress have been retained in the daily costume, and both of these are woven on the indigenous loom. They are the *chumpi* (woven belt), and the *ch'uspa*, an elaborately woven bag used to carry *coca* leaves. Worn hanging from the shoulder, neck or waist, the *ch'uspa* is an essential accessory due to the tremendous socio-cultural importance of *coca*. (See Glossary.)

Many garments have fallen into disuse as the men are adopting modern dress. However, due to the warmth they provide, two garments are universally worn in the highlands. Of Andean origin, the poncho seems to have been developed some time after the Spanish conquest.[8] The *chullo* or *lluchu* on the other hand, is a knitted cap with ear flaps, derived from the traditional *ch'uku*, a conical hat.

Women's clothes have retained more pre-Hispanic elements, although some garments have undergone considerable modification. The *aksu*, for example, was the Inca woman's tunic. When the Spanish initiated dress codes in the 18th century, women began wearing dresses called *almillias*. Quechua women modified the *aksu* to a rectangular cloth which is now worn in the back as a kind of "overskirt." Some women fold it like a fan and hang it decoratively over the belt. Others simply fold the top third of it over the belt and wear it in the back. A third method of wearing the *aksu* is to bring one corner over the shoulder, pull one corner under the opposite armpit and pin them in front. The *aksu* then covers the entire backside and is secured by the belt. Still an important feature of Quechua costume, the *aksu* is usually elaborately patterned.

The *lliclla* or *awayo*, a large square cloth worn by both Aymara and Quechua women, is wrapped around the shoulders and pinned together in front. Formerly the garment was fastened with a silver, gold or copper pin called a *topo* or *pichi*, but today the pins are used only for festive occasions. *Llicllas* are also used as carrying cloths to tote goods and babies. In addition to, or in place of the *lliclla*, some women wear a *rebozo*, a shawl made of embroidered, commercial cloth.

Aymara women once wore a large, gathered skirt called an *urku*, and a shirt much like the men's. The *pollera*, a similar skirt made of industrial cloth, is now more widely used. For fiestas, several colorful *polleras* are worn so that when dancing, the successive layers of colors are revealed.

---

(opposite) *A woman from Tarabuco. The* aksu *(overskirt) covers the back of her* almillia *(dress). Woven hair ties hang down from her braids, partially concealing the* aksu. *She uses her* llicilla *as a carrying cloth which is slung across her back.*

Some women carry coca in a *ch'uspa* and others use a small woven cloth called a *tari* or *incuña*.

Hats are universally used in the highlands and deserve special mention. All people under the Inca realm were commanded to maintain their regional dress, especially their headcloth, even if they moved or joined the army. After the Spanish arrived, Andeans began wearing European-style hats. Today an incredible variety of hats are found throughout Bolivia, and people can still be identified by their headgear. The *p'anta*, a headcloth of pre-Hispanic origin, continues to be worn by some women along with the hat.

Sandals called *ojotas* are worn by all. Once made from llama leather, they are now fashioned from old tires.

(left) *An Aymara woman from the Leque region wearing an* urku *(gathered skirt), an almillia (shirt), and carrying her baby in an* awayo *(carrying cloth).*

Bolivian weavings vary greatly from region to region in style, technique and use. The areas described here represent some of the important weaving centers of Bolivia. The names usually refer to small central villages, although most weaving occurs in the surrounding rural areas.

# REGIONS

Charazani

Calamarca

Pacajes

Bolivar

Potolo
Tarabuco

Calcha

# REGIONS

Bolivian weavings vary greatly from region to region in style, technique and use. The areas described here represent some of the important weaving centers of Bolivia. The names usually refer to small central villages, although most weaving occurs in the surrounding rural areas.

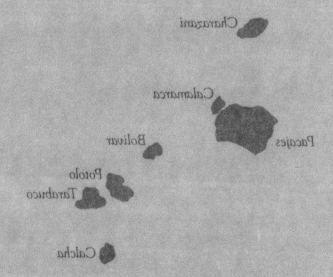

Charazani

Calamarca

Pacajes

Bolivar

Potolo

Tarabuco

Calcha

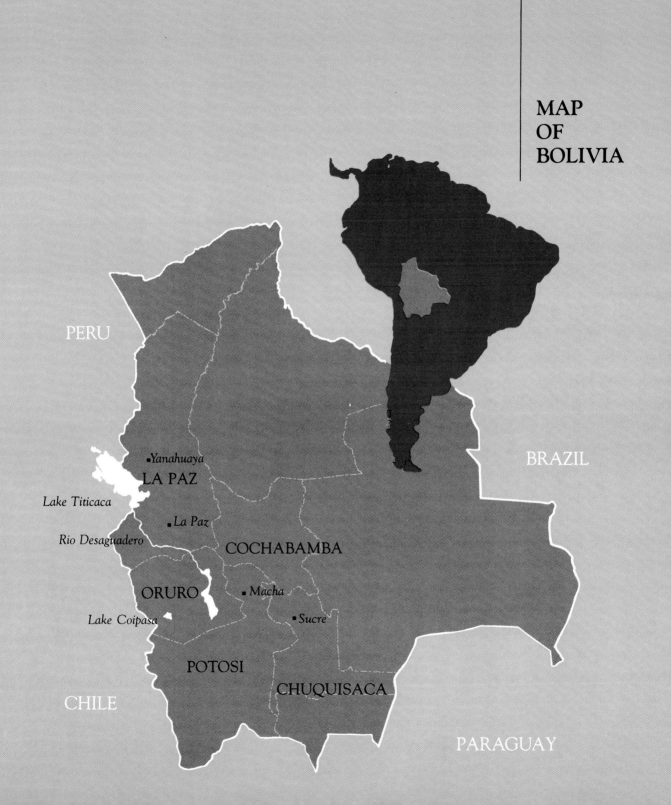

MAP
OF
BOLIVIA

PERU

BRAZIL

Yanahuaya

LA PAZ

Lake Titicaca

La Paz

Rio Desaguadero

COCHABAMBA

ORURO

Macha

Sucre

Lake Coipasa

POTOSI

CHUQUISACA

CHILE

PARAGUAY

# BOLÍVAR

*Important textiles have been handed down from generation to generation among the people of Bolívar. The old weavings show an exceptional tradition of weaving and natural dyeing.*

(upper right) *Detail of no. 20, a Bolívar ceremonial poncho.* (lower right) *A woman from the Bolívar region.* (opposite) *Detail of no. 2, a Bolívar ceremonial poncho.*

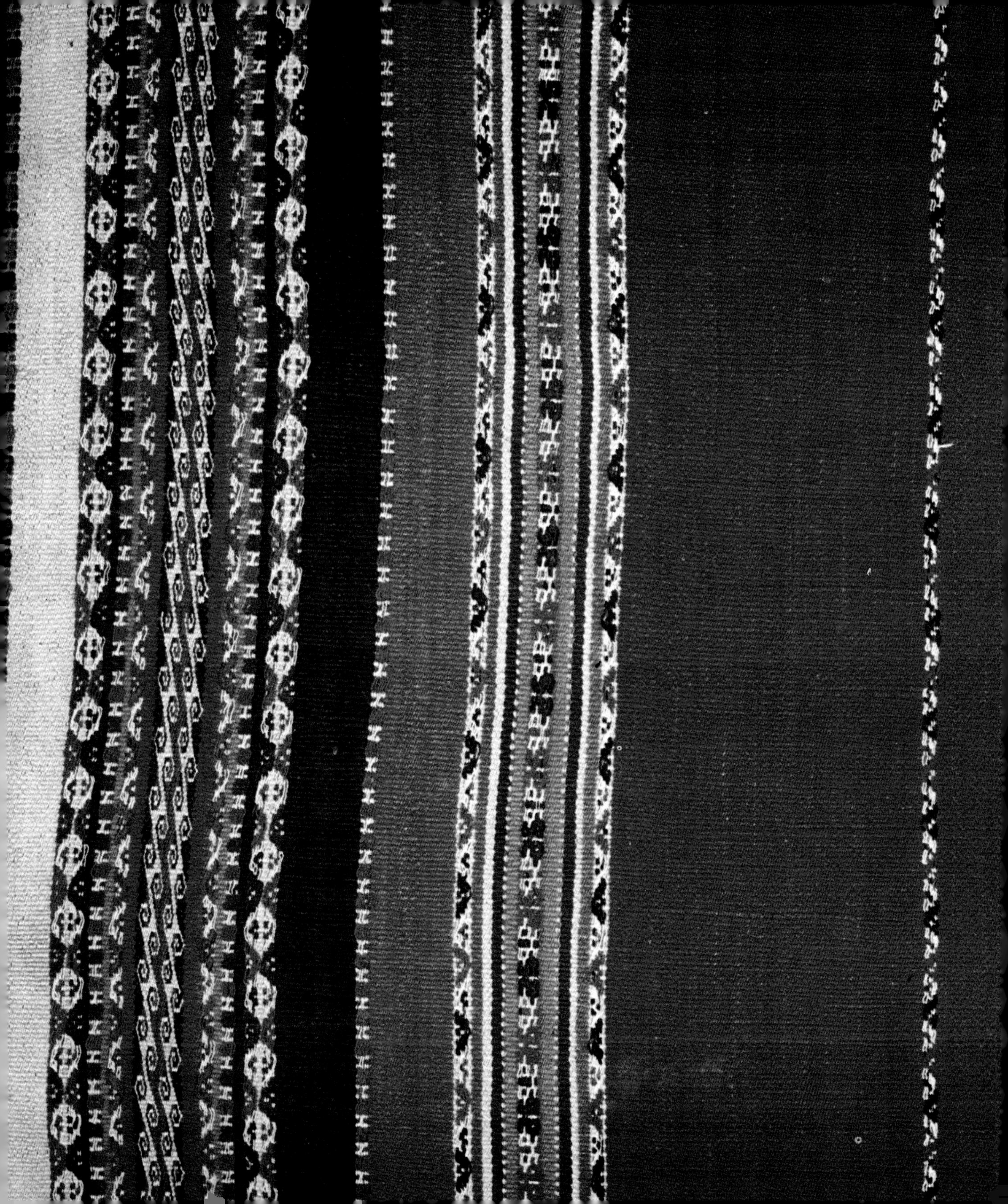

The people of the region of Bolívar have maintained a long and unbroken tradition of weaving excellence. Until recently, they strongly adhered to the Aymara custom of preserving and using old textiles, and consequently a remarkable number of matrimonial and ceremonial pieces have survived from as far back as the early 19th century. These pieces enable us to see an evolution of design which occurred in Bolívar over the last 150 years, along with a linguistic change from Aymara to Quechua.

The oldest of these ceremonial pieces reveal the women's exceptional skill at natural dyeing and are certainly among the most extraordinary textiles to be found in Bolivia today. The large matrimonial *aksus* display impressive compositions of design bands interspersed with monochrome lines. Each piece contains several weave structures. The *lymi linku*, an undulating floral motif woven in warp-patterned double cloth, often forms the main band which is surrounded by auxiliary lines of complementary and derived warps. The bride wears her *aksu* hanging from a woven matrimonial belt and around her shoulders she fastens a matrimonial *lliclla* of the same style. A plain or patterned rectangular cloth called a *llacoya* rests on the shoulders of the groom. Today, these pieces are owned by only a few families who rent them out for local weddings.

Ceremonial ponchos and *ch'uspas* were also woven during this early period to be worn by local chieftains during councils. The ponchos are small (about one meter square) and decorative, indicating a ceremonial rather than utilitarian function. The *ch'uspas* are elaborately ornamented with tassels and little pockets.

A distinct change in weaving design and technique occurred in the Bolívar region some time after the turn of the century. Instead of the narrow lines of traditional Aymara motifs which characterized the previous period, we now find bold representations of condors, *intis* (sun symbols) and cows. These pieces, called *kurti*, were also woven for ceremonial purposes but contain bright aniline dyes instead of the soft natural colors of their predecessors. The patterned areas are woven in wide bands of warp-patterned double cloth.

The contemporary weaving and costume of Bolívar are typical of many of the Quechuas of northern Potosí and southern Cochabamba. Double cloths and complementary warp weaves predominate with figures of birds, animals and *intis*. Both men and women weave actively; pride and excellence in weaving is still very much evident in the area.

## TINKU

In Bolívar, as in many rural towns of the central Bolivian highlands, a festival called *Tinku* takes place several times each year. *Tinku* is a Quechua word meaning encounter or gathering. This festival centers around a traditional type of boxing.

A few days before the fighting starts, Indians from the surrounding rural regions begin coming into Bolívar. The various community groups, accompanied by hired musicians, enter the town, dancing

(above) *Boxing at the* Tinku *festival in Bolívar.*

the festivities. Before each cupful of liquor or handful of *coca,* a bit is thrown on the ground as an offering to *Pachamama, Mother Earth.*[9]

Once the sunset ceremony is completed, the fighting may begin. The participants of two communities confront each other shouting and cursing until someone from each side jumps into the middle. The opponents, who must be of comparable age and state of drunkenness, begin by swinging their arms in a kind of ritualistic dance. Eventually someone lands the first blow and the fighting lasts until one man is down. The fighters are well protected by *monteras* (stiff, cowhide helmets), leather belts, and woven bands which they wrap around their fists. Hard boxing gloves called *ñukus* were once worn but are now prohibited because of the injuries and even deaths they caused.

The wives of the fighters are usually nearby, trying to pull their husbands out of the fighting. This role of the wives is partially symbolic, as the women soon begin their own fighting matches.

The drinking, dancing and fighting may continue for a week or more. During this time, many of the hostilities which have developed over the year between various groups are worked out through the fighting.

and drinking, and dressed in their finest clothes. The women wear several very wide dresses and display their wealth by hanging many *licllas* and silver pieces from their carrying cloths. Some families bring a burro loaded down with weavings, silver and other family treasures.

Upon arriving in Bolívar, the groups perform a short ceremony in the little church. Another brief rite is held on a nearby hilltop shrine at sunset. Much drinking and *coca* chewing accompany

# CALAMARCA

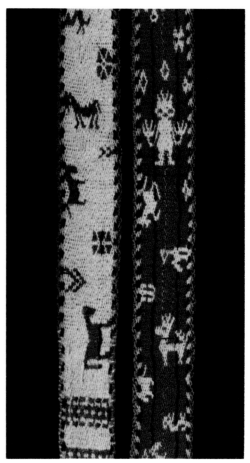

*Calamarqueños wear special ceremonial dress when they take their turn as* mallku *(chieftain) and* t'allamama *(wife of the mallku). Their wide, woven belts display motifs symbolizing the environment, the traditions and the history of Calamarca.*

(left) *The* t'allamama *(chieftain's wife) in full ceremonial dress.* (above) *Detail of no. 32, a Calamarca* tesnu *(belt tie). A mythical god, Kusillo,* is depicted along with other figures. (opposite) *Detail of no. 28, a Calamarca* awayo *(mantle).*

In the town of Calamarca, the Indians from many of the surrounding communities once came together annually to dance and celebrate the festival of *Uransaya-Aransaya* (people from below—people from above). The *mallku* (chieftain) represented his community wearing the fine costume of his office, including garments which were handed down from his ancestors. Many of these pieces are still worn by the *mallkus* of today. Most impressive are the wide belts of warp-patterned double cloth, covered with figures of birds, cows, human forms and sometimes even plants. Frequently the *Puerta del Sol* (Gate of the Sun) from the Tiahuanaco ruins south of Lake Titicaca is depicted on the belts. Sometimes the figures are quite bold, and other times they are very tiny, appearing to float on the ample plain ground. Among the finest weavings done in the Calamarca region are narrow bands which display miniature versions of the figures on the belts. These bands, called *tesnus,* are attached to the ends of belts to hold them in place. Often they are woven with a weft of burro or horse hair and this style of weaving is called *uli.*

The ceremonial poncho, having fewer motifs, is augmented by a vicuña scarf and *wichi-wichis* (pompons) which hang from the waist and swing out from the body when the *mallku* dances. A hat, felted from vicuña fibers, completes the costume.

The wife of the *mallku,* the *t'allamama,* is an equally impressive figure. Her *urku,* a very full skirt, is patterned with a number of decorative bands running horizontally across it on a black ground. A wide belt similar to the *mallku*'s holds the *urku* securely in place as she dances, and over her shoulders she wears an *awayo* with the traditional designs of the area. The *t'allamama*'s hat is a two-pointed crown with a black cloth which hangs freely from it. Lastly, the wrists of the *t'allamama* are adorned with *mangetas* (sleevelets).

Because Calamarca is not far from La Paz, the contemporary dress of the region is modern but many of the traditional customs remain. Each year new *mallkus* are chosen and, although *Uransaya-Aransaya* is no longer celebrated, the chieftains still dance locally during fiestas wearing ceremonial garb. Many people have kept their ancestors' clothes, retaining a deep sense of pride in their traditions as they continue to adopt modern ways.

(below) *Detail of no. 30, a Calamarca waka (belt) depicting barley, the sun, and animals.* (opposite) *Calamarqueño wearing a feather hat and playing a cane flute.*

# CALCHA

*Calcha weaving is typified by exceptionally fine textiles with few patterned areas. The yarn is so finely spun that it is often difficult to see the individual threads in a piece with the naked eye.*

(upper right) *A man and woman from the Calcha region.* (lower right) *Detail of no. 103, a Calcha aksu (overskirt).* (opposite) *Detail of no. 36, a Calcha lliclla (mantle).*

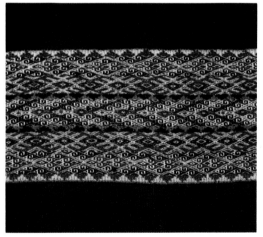

Fine wool spinning is the mark of the textiles from the area around Calcha in southern Potósi. Calcheños are still the best spinners in Bolivia and continue to produce weavings of high quality. Generally their pieces have very little patterned area but what design there is stands out strikingly due to the fine threads and forceful beating of the weft.

(below) *Detail of no. 6, a Calcha poncho. Warp ikat appears in a zig-zag pattern.* (opposite) *Man, woman and child from the Calcha region.*

For example, the *aksus* are entirely black except for two intricately patterned bands, one near each weft selvedge. On these ends one finds the finest warp threads, sometimes over 170 per inch. Though camelid fibers are rarely used, the fabrics often have the shiny appearance of alpaca due to the delicate, tightly spun threads.

Calcheño ponchos are especially handsome and several of them can usually be found in every house. The *panti* is worn daily, its color varying from dark maroon to wine; it is patterned with stripes and tiny design bands of complementary warp weave. The *luto,* or mourning poncho, is always black with few decorative bands. Lastly, the *Boliviano* is woven in very bright stripes and worn mostly for fiestas. Bands called *watado (ikat)* are frequently used on all three types of ponchos.

Because the communities around Calcha sit at relatively low altitudes compared to other weaving regions, ponchos are not always worn in the typical highland manner. Older men fold them diagonally and sling them over one or both shoulders while the younger boys fold them lengthwise and drape them over one shoulder.

Women wear full *almillias,* elaborately embroidered and sequined on the large open sleeves. Very fine, narrow belts, up to five meters long, encircle the waist many times giving the appearance of a wide belt. The *aksu* is fastened in front by a *topo* of Bolivian coins. An embroidered shawl, called a *waita,* completes the outfit.

# CHARAZANI

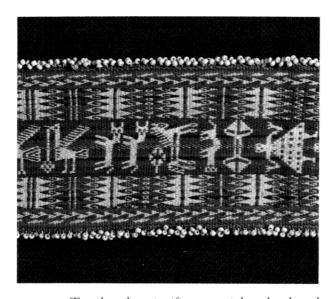

*Textiles play significant social and cultural roles in the lives of the Charazani Indians. Consequently, symbolism and the use of color are important and meaningful factors in their weaving.*

(above) *Detail of no. 42, a Charazani* wincha *(headband).* (right) *A Charazani woman.* (opposite) *Detail of no. 8, a Charazani* pallai aksu *(wedding skirt).*

The decorative motifs used in Charazani represent various aspects of the environment and of the lives of the people. Zoomorphic figures are extremely diverse and anthropomorphic images describe important social events. Rarely simply decorative, geometric motifs have specific correlations to nature. For example, a certain diamond motif depicts the ancient deity, *Inti,* the sun.

The profuse symbolism that developed in Charazani was undoubtedly heavily influenced by the *Callahuayas,* the famous medicine men of the area. These people, who have their own language and customs, have long been known and respected over much of South America for their deep knowledge of herbal and magical healing. It is said that the Incas, recognizing their mastery of these arts, brought some of them to Cuzco to be the court physicians. A number of 19th and 20th century travellers reported seeing them as far away as southern Argentina and northern Colombia, collecting herbs, trading and healing. Even today they can be seen walking the streets of La Paz, carrying a pair of *alforjas,* the woven saddle bags which contain their herbs and amulets.[10]

The influence of the *Callahuayas* is reflected in the scroll motif frequently employed by local weavers. Commonly regarded as a symbol of agricultural fertility, this design is a stylization of the *churu,* a type of land snail. The symbol, however, is also associated with the magic of the *Callahuayas.* One of its forms, the *wajra pallay,* is woven only on the garments of the most experienced practitioners.[11]

The way color is used in the weavings is significant. *Llicllas* are woven with design bands interpersed with monochrome stripes of plain weave. The colors of these stripes represent the levels of land of each community.[12] For example, lower valleys, where corn and wheat are grown, are represented by green stripes. Red signifies the higher fields of potatoes and barley. The pastoral areas, even higher, are shown by maroon bands. Through these color bands and the predominating design motifs, the origin of a piece may be determined.

Cloth is associated with all important social events. The first set of clothes is given at the first haircutting.[13] From that time on, every significant event in the life cycle is marked by the use of special clothing. For example, young girls devote much time to weaving clothing meant to attract a young man. However, on her wedding day the bride wears a matrimonial skirt which has been handed down through the women of her family.

One unique aspect of the women's costumes is the *wincha,* a headband woven in intricate designs and bordered with glass beads. Although of pre-Hispanic origin and apparently once widely used by Quechua women, the *wincha* is presently worn in no other area of Bolivia.

(opposite) *A mountain valley in the Charazani region.*

# PACAJES

Pacajes women of the last century were particularly skilled at spinning and dyeing alpaca. The use of little or no patterned area on a black or brown ground resulted in the simple, dramatic pieces which are characteristic of the Pacajes area.

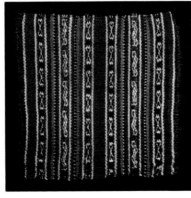

(upper left) Man from Pacajes making bayeta on a treadle loom. (lower left) No. 48, a Pacajes ch'uspa (coca bag). (opposite) Detail of no. 52, an awayo (mantle) from Pacajes.

One of the most important and powerful of the pre-Incan *Colla* realms was the state of Pacasas (now Pacajes). Its strong weaving tradition once produced some of the most exceptional alpaca garments of Bolivia.

Although present-day Pacajes textiles are quite ordinary, 19th century weaving of

the area was of extraordinary quality. Special alpaca ponchos (*challapatas*), worn only by the *hilacatas* (chieftains), have a silky sheen and drape elegantly over the shoulders. The black ground is interrupted by the striped areas; rarely are design motifs used. A striking effect is achieved by the subtle use of natural dyes in the stripes. Cochineal was a favorite dye, producing colors ranging from pale pink to deep carmine.

The *hilacata* wears an elaborate costume. Over his shoulders he wears a small *ponchito* and a large poncho is folded lengthwise, over one shoulder. The two ends of the poncho are pulled across the front and back of the body and tied on the side. A vicuña scarf encircles the neck and crosses in the back. Completing the costume is a highly decorated *ch'uspa,* a wood and silver *baston de manda* (staff of office) and a *chicote* (braided rope).

The women once dressed in equally fine garments. Their *llicllas,* also of alpaca, have a black or brown ground and narrow designs in the same colors as the ponchos. The *urku* is quite full and made of shiny black alpaca. A wide, colorful belt stands out against the darker clothes.

The people of Pacajes were adept spinners and their clothes reflect the possibilities available through the use of alpaca. Today we are familiar with the furry alpaca sweaters and blankets exported from the Andean countries. However, the cloths of Pacajes show that by selecting the best fibers and spinning them finely, fabrics as smooth and refined as silk can be woven from alpaca.

# POTOLO

Potolo weaving is marked by the use of real and phantasmal images from nature. Over the years, changes in local fashion have strongly affected these motifs.

(left) *Potolo woman working at an oblique loom.* (above) *Detail of no. 11, a* lliclla (mantle) *from the Potolo region.* (opposite) *Detail of no. 54, a* capote (festival poncho) *from the Potolo region.*

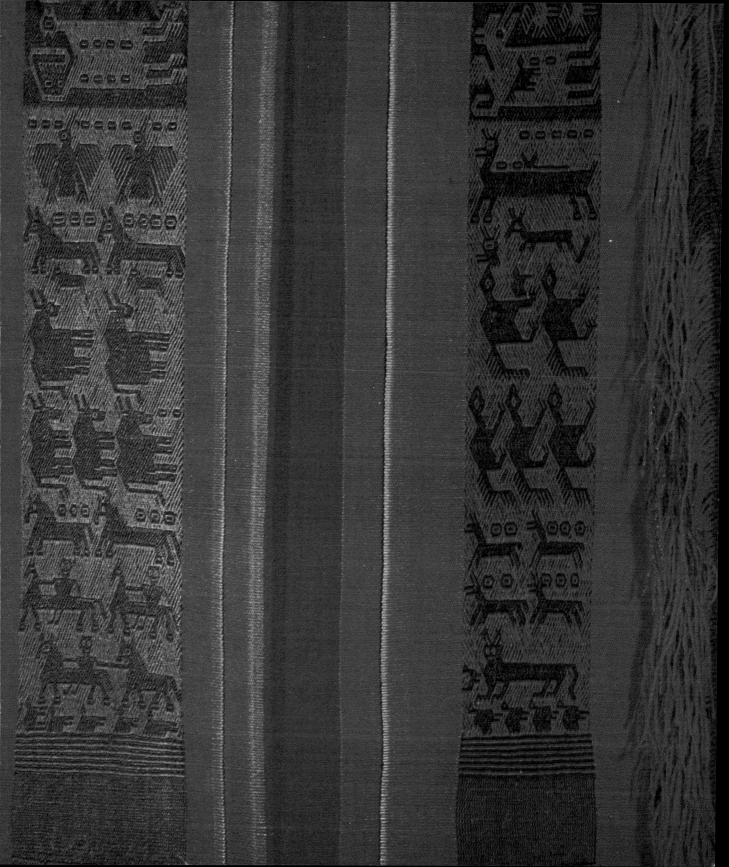

The textiles woven in the region generally referred to as Potolo are among the most graphically expressive weavings of Bolivia. Characterized by numerous birds and animals, these textiles show the light, easy-going sense of humor of the Quechua people. One finds fantastic creatures such as winged, four-legged figures, headless or multi-headed animals, and even birds wearing human clothes. Many animals have comical or mischievous expressions on their faces. Frequently one figure is woven inside another as if it has been eaten or as if the animal has a baby in its belly. Scenes from nature may be portrayed, such as a bird catching a small animal. Humans sometimes appear but it is interesting to note that plants are rarely depicted. On the other hand, *inti,* the sun, is a popular motif.

Unlike other areas where decorative designs are usually woven in bands, the figures on Potolo weavings may occur in a seemingly random pattern, entirely covering a piece. Spatial relationships are free-form. Figures can be arranged upside down or sideways, in any pose, and may vary in size from very large ones, which cover almost half the width of the piece, to tiny creatures the size of a thumbnail.

The oldest known pieces of the Potolo region may be dated after the turn of the century.[14] The figures on these older pieces are diverse, refined and ordered. As time progressed, the weavers began to design more freely. Figures on the weavings between fifteen and thirty years old are extremely animated and randomly arranged. In recent years the women have begun weaving smaller patterned areas and the figures, almost always birds, are lined up in an ordered fashion.

Beginning weavers make little practice pieces called *sakas,* on which they try weaving different motifs to learn how to form figures. However, when the weaver actually makes a piece there is no graph and no fixed thread count for any one motif.

Potoleños wear the typical clothes of the Quechuas but some of their traditional pieces are unique to the area. The men, until recently, wore large festival ponchos called *capotes.* Four detailed bands decorate these ponchos which are fringed with long yarns that swirl when the men dance. The costume is augmented by a tiny festival *ch'uspa* adorned with fancy tassels up to a half meter long.

While little is understood of the symbology of Potolan weaving, we do know that it is, as in most of Bolivia, an important tradition. According to one story, years ago when Potolan women came of weaving age, they would go to a certain cave to spend the night. There, they made love with the devil who gave them the inspiration to weave the strange dragons and monsters which once characterized their pieces.

(opposite) *Man from the Potolo region.*

# TARABUCO

The clothes of Tarabuco make up one of the most unique and colorful costumes of the highlands. Several of the unusual elements of dress occur nowhere else in Bolivia.

(left) *Sunday market in Tarabuco.* (below) *Detail of no. 68, a mourning* ch'uspa *(coca bag) from the Tarabuco area.* (opposite) *Detail of no. 72, a* pallai unku *(ceremonial ponchito) from the Tarabuco area.*

48

The Tarabucan costume reflects the strong influence of Spanish tradition on native Bolivian clothes. Both men and women wear hard leather hats called *monteras,* styled after the helmets of the conquistadors. The women sometimes wear a boat-shaped hat of European influence, covered with ric-rac and sequins. The most widely used zoomorphic motif on their weaving is the horse, an animal of European origin, although it is commonly found side by side with the indigenous llama. Tarabucans also strongly adhere to the Catholic custom of wearing black clothes, called *luto,* for periods of mourning and therefore everyone has a set of black clothes including, for men, a black *ch'uspa.* These clothes are identical in layout and motif to the everyday garments, except that they are woven in black.

Tarabucan women weave the patterned areas of their pieces in a type of complementary warp weave, but the technique is complicated by the use of two different materials for the warp elements. A fine white commercial thread is warped along with the coarser, hand-spun wool. Because the wool yarns are considerably thicker than the white ones, the colored motifs appear in relief. These designs are found on *aksus, ch'uspas,* and sometimes on *llicllas,* but never on ponchos which are woven in plain stripes. Colors, as well as design motifs, vary considerably from one community to another and local people recognize where others come from by their dress. For example, the northern end of the region, around Presto, is warmer and lower than the southern end. The people there weave floral and

geometric designs in sunny colors. As one moves south, the colors become darker and the ponchos larger, reflecting the colder climate; the design motifs are characteristically horses and llamas.

The costume of the region is highly stylized and recognizable as distinctly Tarabucan. A tiny poncho called a *k'onga unku* is worn around the shoulders, under the main poncho. For festivals, a *paillai unku* with elaborate designs is worn over the poncho. Hanging on the back side from a wide leather belt is the *cintera unku,* a small square cloth. The white pants are especially wide and fall just below the knees. Blue shirts and *almillias* are embroidered with black yarn in a zig-zag motif. The Tarabucans are also one of the few groups in Bolivia whose men maintain the ancient custom of wearing long hair, usually elaborately braided.

Although much Spanish influence has been absorbed into their culture, the Tarabucans have retained a strong sense of identity. They were among the fiercest fighters against Spain during the War of Independence, and it is said that they used to rip out the hearts of their victims and drink the heart's blood, thereby taking on the courage of their enemies.

(opposite) *Tarabucan boys at the Sunday market.*

## 1. WOMAN'S MATRIMONIAL COSTUME
Bolívar, Dept. of Cochabamba
Mid-19th c.: *aksu* (overskirt), *lliclla* (mantle), and belt. Contemporary: dress, *p'anta* (headcloth), hat, sandals, and *topo* (pin). The dress and *p'anta* are made from wool *bayeta*. The wool *aksu*, *lliclla* and belt were handed down from mother to daughter for matrimonial use. They are still used today along with contemporary clothes. The felted wool hat is adorned with hatbands with supplementary wefts.
*Lent by UCLA Museum of Cultural History. Gift of Nancy and Richard Bloch.*

## 2. MAN'S CEREMONIAL COSTUME
Bolívar, Dept. of Cochabamba
Mid-19th c.: poncho, *ch'uspa* (coca bag). Contemporary: jacket, *chullo* (knit cap), pants, hat, and sandals.
The sheep's wool poncho and alpaca *ch'uspa* are ceremonial heirlooms worn by local leaders to attend community meetings. Both are woven in complementary warp, derived warp, and double cloth on warp-faced plain weave. The pants and jacket are made from wool *bayeta* and have cotton, machine-stitched embroidery. The *chullo* is wool.
*Poncho and* ch'uspa *lent by Nancy Bloch.*

## 3. MAN'S *TINKU* COSTUME
Bolívar, Dept. of Cochabamba
Contemporary
The pants, vest and jacket are made from wool *bayeta*. A sash woven from synthetic fibers in tapestry weave is used around the waist. Special fighting gear include the *montera* (a hard, cowhide helmet), a *cinteron* (wide, leather belt), and a *ñuku* (a stiff boxing glove made from wool).

## 4. MAN'S *TINKU* COSTUME
Bolívar, Dept. of Cochabamba
Similar to Costume no. 3. A double cloth belt filled with sand and lead is wrapped around the hand for fighting.

*(opposite) Condor motif. Detail of no. 123, a belt from Challa.*

## 5. WOMAN'S CEREMONIAL COSTUME
Calamarca, Dept. of La Paz
Early 20th c.
This costume is worn for special festivals by the *t'allamama*, wife of the *mallku* (chieftain). The cotton jacket is embroidered with cotton threads and sequins. The The wide wool belt is covered with numerous figures and is woven in double cloth. The *urku* (skirt) and the *lliclla* (mantle) are wool and have design bands of complementary warp and warp-faced plain weave. The *montera* (hat) is a two-pointed crown with a cotton cloth covering. Wool *mangetas* (sleevelets) are worn on the forearms. The shirt is wool, woven in balanced plain weave. The *topo* (pin) is silver.
*Belt lent by William Siegal and Arthur Tracht.*

## 6. MAN'S COSTUME
Calcha, Dept. of Potosí
Contemporary
The pants and shirt are wool. A long wool cloth, called a *señor*, encircles the waist partially concealing a leather *cinteron* (belt). Bands of complementary warp weave and *ikat* decorate the poncho. Ceremonial *ojotas* (sandals) are made from llama leather with metal studs on the soles. The felted hat is adorned with a small hatband with supplementary wefts. The *ch'uspa* (coca bag) is woven in complementary warp weave.

## 7. WOMAN'S COSTUME
Calcha, Dept. of Potosí
Contemporary
The dress and *waita* (shawl) are made from *paño*, a commercial wool cloth. The sleeves of the dress are elaborately embroidered and decorated with sequins. The *waita* is fastened with a *topo* (pin) of nickel coins. The *aksu* (overskirt) is woven in complementary warp on a warp-faced plain weave. The belt is woven in complementary warp weave and is over four meters (13 feet) long. The felted hat has hatbands with supplementary wefts.

## 8. WOMAN'S MATRIMONIAL COSTUME
Charazani region, Dept. of La Paz
Early 20th c.
The red wool *unkuchana* (shirt) is partially covered by the *añaku* (underskirt) which is made from alpaca. The *pallai aksu* (wedding skirt) is worn over the lower part of the *añaku* and is woven from alpaca with design bands of complementary warp weave. The *lliclla* (mantle) has bands of double cloth and is held in place with the silver *topos* (pins). A belt made from alpaca is wrapped around the waist. The *wincha* (headband) is woven in double cloth and ornamented with glass beads.

## 9. MAN'S CEREMONIAL COSTUME
Achiri, Prov. of Pacajes, Dept. of La Paz
Mid-19th c.: poncho, belt, and *ch'uspa* (coca bag). Early 20th c.: ponchito. Contemporary: pants, jacket, *chullo* (knitted cap), sandals, *chicote* (braided leather rope), and *baston de manda* (staff of office). This is the costume of the *hilacata* (chieftain). The pants, jacket and beaded *chullo* are wool. The other woven pieces are pure alpaca. A ponchito is worn on the shoulders. The *challapata* (ceremonial poncho) is folded over one shoulder and tied at the waist on the other side. The *ch'uspa* is woven in complementary warp on warpfaced plain weave. As a sign of office, a *baston de manda* and a *chicote* are carried in the hand. A *wichi-wichi* (pompons) hangs from the belt.

## 10. MAN'S FESTIVAL COSTUME
Potolo region, Dept. of Potosí
Mid-20th c.
All pieces are made from sheep's wool. The pants and shirt are *bayeta*. The *capote* (festival poncho) displays bands of numerous animals. The *ch'uspa* (coca bag) has long wrapped tassels. A *lliclla* (mantle) is rolled up and worn around the waist. The design motifs are done in complementary warp weave. The felted hat is adorned with hatbands woven in various techniques.

## 11. WOMAN'S FESTIVAL COSTUME
Potolo region, Dept. of Potosí
Mid-20th c.
All woven pieces are wool. The decorative *aksu* (overskirt) is worn in the back and held by a *cañara* (thick, soumak-weave belt). Both the *aksu* and the *lliclla* (mantle) are woven in complementary warp on warp-faced plain weave. The felted hat is adorned with hatbands woven in various techniques.

## 12. MAN'S COSTUME
Candelaria, Tarabuco region, Dept. of Chuquisaca
Contemporary
This costume is woven in wool and has several unusual features. The pants are short and wide and are woven in a type of herringbone twill. The designs on the shirt are made with a simple running embroidery stitch. A *cintera unku* (waist cloth) hangs from the waist in back. Another *unku* is worn like a tiny poncho. The wide leather belt is tooled and ornamented with metal rivets and has compartments for money and papers. The dark-striped poncho and the horse motif *ch'uspa* (coca bag) identify the costume as being from the southern Tarabuco area. The leather *montera* (helmet) is adorned with tassels and sequins.

## 13. WOMAN'S COSTUME
Villa Villa, Tarabuco region, Dept. of Chuquisaca
Mid-20th c.
The wool dress is embroidered with black yarn. The designs of the *aksu* (overskirt), the *lliclla* (mantle), and the belt are woven in complementary warp weave; the colored yarns are wool and the white threads are cotton. Glass beads and tassels made from horse hair ornament the *tulma* (wrapped hair tie). A silver *topo* (pin) fastens the *lliclla*. Sequins and embroidery embellish the boat-shaped *montera* (hat).

## 14. URU MAN'S COSTUME
Iruito, Dept. of La Paz
Contemporary
This wool costume is worn at night for fishing and duck hunting, protecting the men from the cold night air. The coarse, heavy *ira* (tunic) is woven in warp-faced plain weave. The pants are woven in a twill weave. *Mangetisas* (sleeves) and the *chullo* (cap) are knitted from sheep's wool.

## 15. WOMAN'S COSTUME
Bolívar, Dept. of Cochabamba
Contemporary
The woven articles are made from wool. The skirt, jacket and *p'anta* (headcloth) are woven in balanced plain weave, and stitched with machine embroidery. The *lliclla* (mantle) is woven in complementary warp on warp-faced plain weave. The hat is felted and adorned with hatbands with supplementary wefts.

## 16. MAN'S COSTUME
Macha, Dept. of Potosí
Contemporary
All garments are made from wool except for the weft-faced *chalina* (sash) which is made from wool and cotton. The belt is double cloth, the *ch'uspa* (coca bag) is complementary warp weave, and the hatbands have supplementary wefts. The pants and jacket are made from *bayeta* woven on a treadle loom. The *chullo* (knitted cap) is worn under a wool felt hat.

## 17. WOMAN'S COSTUME
Macha, Dept. of Potosí
Contemporary
The woven articles are wool. The *aksu* (overskirt) and the *lliclla* (mantle) are woven in complementary warp on warp-faced plain weave. The hat is felted wool and is adorned with supplementary weft hatbands. A *cañara* (thick, soumak-weave belt) is worn around the waist.
*Aksu lent by William Siegal and Arthur Tracht.*

18. MAN'S COSTUME
Yanahuaya, Dept. of La Paz
Contemporary
The pants, shirt and vest are made from wool *bayeta,* and the warp-faced plain weave *mantilla* (carrying cloth) is made from llama's wool. The designs on the *ch'uspa* (coca bag) are formed with supplementary warps. The belt is woven in complementary warp weave. The hat is felted wool.

19. WOMAN'S COSTUME
Yanahuaya, Dept. of La Paz
Contemporary
The woven articles are wool. The wide belt is woven with many figures in complementary warp weave. The *lliclla* (mantle) has no design area and is entirely woven in warp-faced plain weave. The wrap-around skirt and the shirt are woven in balanced plain weave. The hat is wool felt.

20. CEREMONIAL PONCHO
Bolívar, Dept. of Cochabamba
Mid-19th c.
Sheep's wool and llama. Double cloth, complementary warp, and derived warp on warp-faced plain weave; alternating S/Z-spun warps at outer weft selvedges; woven fringe.
Warp: 98 cm.; weft: 96 cm.

21. MATRIMONIAL *AKSU*
(woman's overskirt)
Bolívar, Dept. of Cochabamba
Mid-19th c.
Alpaca. Complementary warp and derived warp on warp-faced plain weave; alternating S/Z-spun warps at outer weft selvedges.
Warp: 105 cm.; weft: 152 cm.

22. *LLACOYA* (man's matrimonial mantle)
Bolívar, Dept. of Cochabamba
Late 19th c. (?)
Sheep's wool and alpaca. Complementary warp on warp-faced plain weave; alternating S/Z-spun warps at lower weft selvedge.
Warp: 137 cm.; weft: 72 cm.

23. MATRIMONIAL *LLICLLA*
(woman's mantle)
Bolívar, Dept. of Cochabamba
Mid-19th c.
Alpaca. Double cloth, complementary warp and derived warp on warp-faced plain weave; tubular border.
Warp: 120 cm.; weft: 115 cm.
*Lent by Jonathan Whitman.*

24. CEREMONIAL *CH'USPA* (coca bag)
Bolívar, Dept. of Cochabamba
Mid-19th c.
Sheep's wool and alpaca. Double cloth, complementary warp and derived warp on warp-faced plain weave; tubular border and tassels.
Warp: 22 cm.; weft: 24 cm.

25. MATRIMONIAL *CHUMPI* (belt)
Bolívar, Dept. of Cochabamba
Mid-19th c.
Alpaca. Double cloth; braiding.
Warp: 160 cm.; weft: 6.5 cm.

26. MATRIMONIAL *LLICLLA*
(woman's mantle)
Bolívar, Dept. of Cochabamba
Early 20th c.
Sheep's wool. Double cloth and complementary warp on warp-faced plain weave.
Warp: 110 cm.; weft: 117 cm.

27. *CHUMPI* (belt)
Bolívar, Dept. of Cochabamba
Early to mid-20th c.
Sheep's wool. Warp-faced double cloth.
Warp: 84 cm.; weft: 17 cm.

28. *AWAYO* (woman's mantle or carrying cloth)
Colquencha, Calamarca region, Dept. of La Paz
Late 19th c. (?)
Alpaca. Complementary warp on warp-faced plain weave; tubular border.
Warp: 187 cm.; weft: 115 cm.

29. *CH'USPA* (coca bag)
Santiago de Llallagua, Calamarca region, Dept. of La Paz
Early 20th c.
Sheep's wool. Complementary warp on warp-faced plain weave; tubular border; fringe.
Warp: 20 cm.; weft: 22 cm.

30. CEREMONIAL *WAKA* (belt)
Santiago de Llallagua, Calamarca region, Dept. of La Paz
Late 19th c. (?)
Alpaca. Warp-faced double cloth; braiding.
Warp: 176 cm.; weft: 12.5 cm.
*Lent by William Siegal and Arthur Tracht.*

31. CEREMONIAL *HONDA* (sling)
Micaya, Calamarca region, Dept. of La Paz
Early 20th c. (?)
Alpaca. Interlocked tapestry weave; braiding.
Warp: 125 cm.; weft: 3.5 cm.

32. *TESNU* (belt tie)
Colquencha, Calamarca region, Dept. of La Paz
Early 20th c.
Sheep's wool warp, horse hair weft. Warp-faced double cloth; braiding.
Warp: 62 cm.; weft: 2 cm.

33. *WICHI-WICHI* (pompons)
Colquencha, Calamarca region, Dept. of La Paz
Mid-20th c.
Sheep's wool. Weft-faced plain weave; braiding.
Length: 32 cm.

34. FEATHER DANCING HAT
Micaya, Calamarca region, Dept. of La Paz
Mid-20th c.
Flamingo feathers, wool felt hat.
Diameter: 70 cm.; Height: 40 cm.
*Lent by William Siegal and Arthur Tracht.*

35. *PHULLO* (blanket)
Calcha region, Dept. of Potosí
Mid-20th c.
Sheep's wool. Complementary warp
weave.
Warp: 162 cm.; weft: 161 cm.

36. *LLICLLA* (woman's mantle)
Yawisla, Calcha region, Dept. of Potosí
Early 20th c. (?)
Sheep's wool. Complementary warp on
warp-faced plain weave; tubular border.
Warp: 94 cm.; weft: 108 cm.

37. *ALFORJAS* (saddle bags)
Yawisla, Calcha region, Dept. of Potosí
Mid-20th c.
Sheep's wool. Warp *ikat* on warp-faced
plain weave; tubular border; tassels.
Warp: 36 cm.; weft: 34 cm. (each)

38. MOURNING PONCHO
Calcha region, Dept. of Potosí
Mid-20th c.
Sheep's wool. Complementary warp and
warp *ikat* on warp-faced plain weave;
woven fringe.
Warp: 126 cm.; weft: 132 cm.

39. FESTIVAL PONCHO
Calcha region, Dept. of Potosí
Mid-20th c.
Sheep's wool. Complementary warp and
warp *ikat* on warp-faced plain weave;
woven fringe.
Warp: 120 cm.; weft: 122 cm.

40. *LLICLLA* (woman's mantle)
Charazani region, Dept. of La Paz
Early 20th c. (?)
Sheep's wool. Double cloth on warp-faced
plain weave; tubular border.
Warp: 88 cm.; weft: 83 cm.

41. CEREMONIAL PONCHO
Charazani region, Dept. of La Paz
Mid-20th c.
Sheep's wool and alpaca. Double cloth on
warp-faced plain weave; woven fringe.
Warp: 126 cm.; weft 120 cm.

42. *WINCHA* (woman's headband)
Charazani region, Dept. of La Paz
Early to mid-20th c.
Alpaca. Double cloth; beadwork on weft
selvedges.
Warp: 44 cm.; weft: 6.5 cm.

43. *TARI* (small carrying cloth)
Charazani region, Dept. of La Paz
Mid-20th c.
Sheep's wool and cotton. Double cloth on
warp-faced plain weave; tubular border.
Warp: 53 cm.; weft: 50 cm.

44. *WINCHA* (woman's headband)
Charazani region, Dept. of La Paz
Early to mid-20th c.
Sheep's wool. Double cloth, beadwork on
weft selvedges.
Warp: 48 cm.; weft: 4.5 cm.

45. *WAKA* (ceremonial belt)
Santiago de Machaca, Prov. of Pacajes,
Dept. of La Paz
Mid- to late 19th c.
Alpaca. Complementary warp on warp-
faced plain weave.
Warp: 134 cm.; weft: 16 cm.

46. *WAKA* (ceremonial belt)
Huaripuyo, Prov. of Pacajes,
Dept. of La Paz
Late 19th c. to early 20th c.
Sheep's wool (?). Complementary warp
weave.
Warp: 102 cm.; weft: 6.5 cm.

47. *WICHI-WICHI* (pompons)
Achiri, Prov. of Pacajes, Dept. of La Paz
Late 19th c. (?)
Alpaca. Tapestry weave; braiding; tassels.
Length: 75 cm.

48. *CH'USPA* (coca bag)
Prov. of Pacajes, Dept. of La Paz
Mid-19th c. (?)
Alpaca. Complementary warp on warp-
faced plain weave; tubular border; fringe.
Warp: 21 cm.; weft: 19 cm.

49. PONCHO
Achiri, Prov. of Pacajes, Dept. of La Paz
Mid-19th c.
Alpaca. Warp-faced plain weave; woven
fringe.
Warp: 172 cm.; weft: 126 cm.

50. PONCHITO (small ceremonial
poncho)
Mikani, Prov. of Pacajes, Dept. of La Paz
Late 19th c.
Alpaca. Complementary warp on warp-
faced plain weave; alternating bands of
S/Z-spun warps at outer weft selvedges;
woven fringe.
Warp: 79 cm.; weft: 80 cm.

51. PONCHO
Achiri, Prov. of Pacajes, Dept. of La Paz
Early to mid-19th c. (?)
Alpaca. Warp-faced plain weave; woven
fringe.
Warp: 160 cm.; weft: 118 cm.

52. *AWAYO* (woman's mantle)
Huaripuyo, Prov. of Pacajes,
Dept. of La Paz
Early to mid-19th c.
Alpaca. Complementary warp on warp-
faced plain weave; alternating bands of
S/Z-spun warps at outer weft selvedges.
Warp: 102 cm.; weft: 51 cm.

53. *SURI* (feather headdress)
Mikani, Prov. of Pacajes, Dept. of La Paz
Early 20th c. (?)
Rhea feathers, cane.
Diameter: 170 cm.
*Lent by William Siegal and Arthur Tracht.*

54. *CAPOTE* (festival poncho)
Potolo region, Dept. of Potosí
Early 20th c.
Sheep's wool. Complementary warp on
warp-faced plain weave; woven fringe.
Warp: 103 cm.; weft: 114 cm.

55. FESTIVAL *AKSU*
(woman's overskirt)
Potolo region, Dept. of Potosí
Early 20th c.
Sheep's wool. Complementary warp on
warp-faced plain weave; tubular border.
Warp: 85 cm.; weft: 127 cm.

56. *LLICLLA* (woman's mantle)
Janina, Potolo region, Dept. of Potosí
Early to mid-20th c.
Sheep's wool. Complementary warp on
warp-faced plain weave.
Warp: 94 cm.; weft: 89 cm.

57. FESTIVAL *AKSU*
(woman's overskirt)
Potolo region, Dept. of Potosí
Mid-20th c.
Sheep's wool and llama. Complementary
warp on warp-faced plain weave; tubular
border; alternating bands of S/Z-spun
warps at outer weft selvedges.
Warp: 87 cm.; weft: 117 cm.

58. HALF *AKSU* (woman's overskirt)
Potolo region, Dept. of Potosí
Early to mid-20th c.
Sheep's wool and llama. Complementary
warp on warp-faced plain weave; alternat-
ing bands of S/Z-spun warps at lower weft
selvedge.
Warp: 97 cm.; weft: 62 cm.

59. HALF *AKSU* (woman's overskirt)
Janina, Potolo region, Dept. of Potosí
Mid-20th c.
Sheep's wool. Complementary warp on
warp-faced plain weave.
Warp: 73 cm.; weft: 63 cm.

60. HALF *AKSU* (woman's overskirt)
Potolo region, Dept. of Potosí
Early 20th c. (?)
Sheep's wool. Complementary warp on
warp-faced plain weave; alternating bands
of S/Z-spun warps on lower weft selvedge.
Warp: 84 cm.; weft: 66 cm.

61. *WAYACA* (bag)
Potolo region, Dept. of Potosí
Mid-20th c.
Llama. Complementary warp on warp-
faced plain weave.
Warp: 82 cm.; weft: 40 cm.

62. FESTIVAL *CH'USPA* (coca bag)
Potolo region, Dept. of Potosí
Mid-20th c.
Sheep's wool. Complementary warp on
warp-faced plain weave; wrapping; tassels.
Warp: 44.5 cm.; weft: 10 cm.
(including tassels)

63. *SAKA* (sampler)
Rodeo, Potolo region, Dept. of Potosí
Mid-20th c.
Llama. Complementary warp weave;
braiding.
Warp: 32 cm.; weft: 11 cm.

64. *SAKA* (sampler)
Potolo region, Dept. of Potosí
Mid-20th c.
Llama. Complementary warp weave.
Warp: 44.5 cm.; weft: 28 cm.

65. HALF *AKSU* (woman's overskirt)
Villa Villa, Tarabuco region,
Dept. of Chuquisaca
Mid-20th c. (?)
Sheep's wool and cotton. Complementary
warp on warp-faced plain weave; alternat-
ing bands of S/Z-spun warps at lower weft
selvedge; tubular border.
Warp: 114 cm.; weft: 83 cm.
*Lent by Arthur Tracht.*

66. SADDLE BLANKET
Tarabuco region, Dept. of Chuquisaca (?)
Early 20th c. (?)
Alpaca and cotton. Supplementary weft
on warp-faced plain weave; woven fringe.
Warp: 74 cm.; weft: 91 cm.

67. *CINTERA UNKU* (man's waist cloth)
Tarabuco region, Dept. of Chuquisaca
Mid-20th c.
Sheep's wool. Warp-faced plain weave;
woven fringe.
Warp: 52 cm.; weft: 57 cm.

68. *CH'USPA* (coca bag)
Tarabuco region, Dept. of Chuquisaca
Mid-20th c.
Sheep's wool and cotton. Complementary
warp weave; tubular border; tassels.
Warp: 16 cm.; weft: 18 cm.

69. *CH'USPA* (coca bag)
Tarabuco region, Dept. of Chuquisaca
Mid-20th c.
Sheep's wool and cotton. Complementary
warp weave; tubular border; tassels.
Warp: 20 cm.; weft: 18 cm.

70. *CH'USPA* (coca bag)
Tarabuco region, Dept. of Chuquisaca
Mid-20th c.
Sheep's wool and cotton. Complementary
warp weave; tubular border; tassels.
Warp: 15 cm.; weft: 15 cm.

71. *TULMA* (man's hair tie)
Tarabuco region, Dept. of Chuquisaca
Mid-20th c.
Sheep's wool and cotton. Complementary
warp weave; wrapping; pompons.
Warp: 87 cm.; weft: 2 cm.

72. *UNKU* (man's ponchito)
Tarabuco region, Dept. of Chuquisaca
Mid-20th c.
Sheep's wool and cotton. Complementary
warp weave; woven fringe.
Warp: 45 cm.; weft: 59 cm.

73. PONCHO
Dept. of Potosí
Early 20th c. (?)
Sheep's wool and alpaca (?). Warp *ikat* on
warp-faced plain weave; tubular border.
Warp: 160 cm.; weft: 140 cm.

74. *MANTILLA* (ceremonial cloth)
Dept. of La Paz
Late 19th c. (?)
Sheep's wool and alpaca. Supplementary
warp on warp-faced plain weave;
tubular border.
Warp: 94 cm.; weft: 68 cm.

75. CEREMONIAL PONCHO
Provenance unknown
Late 19th c. (?)
Sheep's wool. Complementary warp on
warp-faced plain weave; alternating bands
of S/Z-spun warps at outer weft selvedges;
woven fringe.
Warp: 208 cm.; weft: 196 cm.

76. *TULMA* (woman's hair tie)
Tarabuco region, Dept. of Chuquisaca
Contemporary
Sheep's wool, glass beads and horse hair.
Braiding; wrapping; tassels.
Length: 197 cm.

77. CEREMONIAL PONCHO
Provenance unknown
Mid-19th c. (?)
Alpaca. Complementary warp on warp-
faced plain weave; alternating bands of
S/Z-spun warps at outer·weft selvedges.
Warp: 194 cm.; weft: 148 cm.

78. *MANTILLA* (ceremonial cloth)
Dept. of La Paz
Late 19th c. (?)
Alpaca. Complementary warp and derived
warp on warp-faced plain weave.
Warp: 88 cm.; weft: 84 cm.

79. *UNKU* (man's tunic shirt)
Provenance unknown
Early to mid-19th c. (?)
Alpaca. Warp-faced plain weave; alternat-
ing bands of S/Z-spun warps across entire
piece.
Warp: 73 cm.; weft: 77 cm.

80. *COSTAL* (storage sack)
Potolo region, Dept. of Potosí
Contemporary
Llama. Warp-faced plain weave.
Warp: 94 cm.; weft: 68 cm.

81. CEREMONIAL PONCHO
Provenance unknown
Mid-19th c. (?)
Sheep's wool and alpaca. Supplementary
warp and derived warp on warp-faced plain
weave; alternating bands of S/Z-spun
warps at outer weft selvedges; woven
fringe.
Warp: 180 cm.; weft: 158 cm.

82. PONCHO
Rodeo, Potolo region, Dept. of Potosí
Contemporary
Sheep's wool. Complementary warp on
warp-faced plain weave; tubular border.
Warp: 174 cm.; weft: 128 cm.

83. PONCHITO (small poncho)
Irumsata, Dept. of Potosí
Early to mid-19th c. (?)
Alpaca with silver threads at neck and
border. Warp-faced plain weave; bands of
alternating S/Z-spun warps at outer weft
selvedges; tubular border; braiding.
Warp: 60 cm.; weft: 91 cm.

84. *CH'USPA* (bag)
Found in Bolivia
Post-Conquest, probably 17th c.
Sheep's wool and alpaca (?). Interlocked
and slit tapestry weave.
Warp: 24.5 cm.; weft: 19 cm.

85. *CHUMPI* (belt)
Provenance unknown
Early 20th c. (?)
Sheep's wool. Warp-faced double cloth;
braiding; tubular border.
Warp: 114 cm.; weft: 8 cm.

86. *BALSA* (reed boat)
Isla del Sol, Lake Titicaca
Contemporary
Totora reed.
Height: 254 cm.; length: 127 cm.; width:
62.5 cm.
*Lent by Steve Lannon.*

87. *CH'USPA* (coca bag)
Prov. of Pacajes, Dept. of La Paz
Mid-19th c. (?)
Alpaca. Complementary warp on warp-
faced plain weave; tubular border.
Warp: 15.5 cm.; weft: 15.5 cm.

88. *AKSU* (woman's overskirt)
Challa region, Dept. of Cochabamba
Mid- to late 19th c.
Sheep's wool. Complementary warp on
warp-faced plain weave; alternating S/Z-
spun warps at outer weft selvedges; tubular
border.
Warp: 126 cm.; weft: 147 cm.

89. PONCHO
Provenance unknown
Late 19th c. (?)
Alpaca. Complementary warp on warp-faced plain weave; woven fringe.
Warp: 150 cm.; weft: 140 cm.

90. ALFORJAS (saddle bags)
Provenance unknown
Mid- to late 19th c. (?)
Sheep's wool. Complementary warp on warp-faced plain weave; tubular border; tassels.
Warp: 31 cm.; weft: 31 cm. (each).

91. CH'USPA (coca bag)
Macha region, Dept. of Potosí
Contemporary
Sheep's wool. Complementary warp on warp-faced plain weave; tubular border; crossed warp weave; tassels; wrapping.
Warp (including tassels): 37 cm.; weft: 8 cm.

92. CH'USPA (coca bag)
Prov. of Pacajes, Dept. of La Paz
Late 19th c.
Alpaca. Complementary warp on warp-faced plain weave; tubular border; tassels.
Warp: 16.5 cm.; weft: 27.5 cm.

93. CH'USPA (coca bag)
Leque region, Dept. of Cochabamba
Mid-20th c.
Alpaca. Double cloth and complementary warp on warp-faced plain weave; tubular border; tassels; fringe.
Warp: 20 cm.; weft: 21 cm.

94. CH'USPA (coca bag)
Dept. of Cochabamba (?)
Early to mid-20th c.
Sheep's wool. Warp-faced double cloth; braiding; tassels.
Warp: 25 cm.; weft: 25.5 cm.

95. CH'USPA (coca bag)
Provenance unknown
Mid-19th c. (?)
Alpaca. Complementary warp on warp-faced plain weave; tubular border; tassels.
Warp: 20 cm.; weft: 22 cm.

96. CH'USPA (coca bag)
Prov. of Pacajes, Dept. of La Paz (?)
Early 20th c. (?)
Alpaca. Warp-faced double cloth; tubular border; tassels.
Warp: 19 cm.; weft: 23 cm.

97. CH'USPA (coca bag)
Provenance unknown
Mid-19th c. (?)
Sheep's wool. Complementary warp on warp-faced plain weave; tubular border; tassels.
Warp: 33 cm.; weft: 25 cm.

98. CH'USPA (coca bag)
Dept. of La Paz
Mid- to late 19th c.
Alpaca. Complementary warp on warp-faced plain weave; fringe.
Warp: 19.5 cm.; weft: 22.5 cm.

99. CAPACHO (bag)
Ayata region, Dept. of La Paz
Mid-20th c.
Sheep's wool. Supplementary warp and complementary warp on warp-faced plain weave; braiding; tassels.
Bag—warp: 22 cm.; weft: 34 cm. Strap—warp: 97 cm.; weft: 17.5 cm.

100. TESNU (belt tie)
Leque region, Dept. of Cochabamba
Contemporary
Sheep's wool. Warp-faced double cloth; braiding.
Warp: 104 cm.; weft: 1.5 cm.

101. CINTA (hatband)
Challa region, Dept. of Cochabamba
Contemporary
Cotton. Warp-faced double cloth; braiding.
Warp: 40 cm.; weft: 1 cm.

102. CANAR (lap loom)
Bolívar region, Dept. of Cochabamba
Contemporary
Llama and sheep's wool. Weft wrapping.
Length: 93 cm.; width: 15 cm.

103. HALF AKSU (woman's overskirt)
Calcha region, Dept. of Potosí
Mid-20th c.
Sheep's wool and cotton. Complementary warp on warp-faced plain weave.
Warp: 149 cm.; weft: 70 cm.

104. HORIZONTAL GROUND LOOM
Rodeo, Potolo region, Dept. of Potosí
Contemporary
Sheep's wool. Complementary warp on warp-faced plain weave.
Warp: 51 cm.; weft: 17 cm.

105. HORIZONTAL GROUND LOOM
Chaicuriri, Dept. of Potosí
Contemporary
Sheep's wool. Three-color complementary warp weave.
Warp: 59 cm.; weft: 4.5 cm.

106. BACKSTRAP LOOM
Chaicuriri, Dept. of Potosí
Contemporary
Sheep's wool. Warp-faced plain weave.
Warp: 56 cm.; weft: 23 cm.

107. TWO-HARNESS TREADLE LOOM
Chaicuriri, Dept. of Potosí
Mid-20th c.
Sheep's wool and orlon. Weft-faced plain weave.

108. MATRIMONIAL AKSU
(woman's overskirt)
Bolívar, Dept. of Cochabamba
Mid-19th c. (?)
Sheep's wool and alpaca. Complementary warp on warp-faced plain weave; alternating S/Z-spun warps at outer weft selvedges.
Warp: 131 cm.; weft: 144 cm.

(left) *Detail of no. 61, a* wayaka *(bag) from the Potolo area, showing large figures with smaller ones inside them.*

109. CHUMPI (belt)
Potolo region, Dept. of Potosí
Mid-20th c.
Sheep's wool. Warp-faced double cloth; braiding.
Warp: 130 cm.; weft: 4.5 cm.

110. CHUMPI (belt)
Amarete, Charazani region, Dept. of La Paz
Contemporary
Alpaca (?). Warp-faced double cloth; supplementary warp weave; braiding.
Warp: 152 cm.; weft: 4.5 cm.

111. HALF AKSU (woman's overskirt)
Candelaria, Tarabuco region, Dept. of Chuquisaca
Contemporary
Sheep's wool and cotton. Complementary warp on warp-faced plain weave.
Warp: 107 cm.; weft: 77 cm.

112. PONCHO
Provenance unknown
Early 19th c. (?)
Sheep's wool and cotton. Warp *ikat* on warp-faced plain weave.
Warp: 175 cm.; weft: 140 cm.

113. PONCHO
Caiza region, Dept. of Potosí
Mid-20th c.
Sheep's wool. Warp *ikat* and complementary warp on warp-faced plain weave; woven fringe; alternating bands of S/Z-spun warps at outer weft selvedges.
Warp: 145 cm.; weft: 127 cm.

114. PONCHO
Santiago de Llallagua, Calamarca region, Dept. of La Paz
Late 19th c. (?)
Alpaca. Complementary warp on warp-faced plain weave; woven fringe.
Warp: 91 cm.; weft: 125 cm.

115. LLACOYA (man's ceremonial cape)
Khorpa, Prov. of Ingavi, Dept. of La Paz
Early 19th c. (?)
Alpaca warp, silk and alpaca weft (?).
Warp-faced plain weave; alternating S/Z-spun warps at outer weft selvedges; tubular border.
Warp: 116 cm.; weft: 194 cm.

116. CAPACHO (man's bag)
Charazani region, Dept. of La Paz
Mid-20th c.
Sheep's wool. Double cloth on warp-faced plain weave; tubular border.
Bag—warp: 30 cm.; weft: 42 cm. Strap—warp: 100 cm.; weft: 3 cm.

117. CH'USPA (coca bag)
Dept. of Cochabamba
Mid-20th c. (?)
Sheep's wool. Supplementary warp on warp-faced plain weave; tubular border; tassels.
Warp: 30 cm.; weft: 32 cm.

118. CH'USPA (coca bag)
Challa region, Dept. of Cochabamba
Early to mid-20th c.
Sheep's wool. Warp-faced double cloth; fringe; tassels.
Warp: 15 cm.; weft: 15 cm.

119. LLAMA'S COLLAR WITH BELL AND CH'USPA
Provenance unknown
Late 19th to early 20th c. (?)
Collar and *ch'uspa*: sheep's wool and llama. Complementary warp on warp-faced plain weave; tubular border; braiding. Bell: metal.

120. MONEY POUCH
Provenance unknown
20th c.
Sheep's wool and llama. Knitted.
Length: 34 cm.

121. BOTAS (pair of ceremonial leggings)
Chaicuriri, Dept. of La Paz
Early 20th c. (?)
Sheep's wool. Knitted (?).
Length: 60 cm.; width: 21 cm. (each).

122. SIX CEREMONIAL HONDAS (slings)
Various highland areas
Late 19th to early 20th c.
Sheep's wool and llama. Various weaving and braiding techniques.

123. CHUMPI (belt)
Challa region; Dept. of Cochabamba
20th c.
Sheep's wool and llama. Warp-faced double cloth; braiding.
Warp: 110 cm.; weft: 10 cm.

124. WAKA (belt)
Colquencha, Calamarca region, Dept. of La Paz
Late 19th c. (?)
Sheep's wool and llama. Warp-faced double cloth; braiding.
Warp: 135 cm.; weft: 7 cm.

125. CHUMPI (belt)
Provenance unknown
Late 19th c. (?)
Alpaca. Complementary warp weave; braiding.
Warp: 183 cm.; weft: 5.5 cm.

126. CHUMPI (belt)
Dept. of Potosí
20th c.
Sheep's wool. Warp-faced double cloth; braiding.
Warp: 113 cm.; weft: 3 cm.

127. TULMA (woman's hair tie)
Provenance unknown
Mid-19th c. (?)
Alpaca and vicuña. Braiding; tassels.
Length: 127 cm.

128. LLUCHU (knitted cap)
Santiago de Machaca, Calamarca region, Dept. of La Paz
Mid- to late 19th c.
Sheep's wool. Knitted.
Length: 34.5 cm.; width: 24 cm.
*Lent by Roger Yorke.*

(opposite) *Quechua woman from the Dept. of La Paz.*

# GLOSSARY

AKSU (Que.)—Rectangular cloth which women wear in the back, hanging from the belt or covering the entire back side; a tunic-style dress during the Inca period.

ALFORJAS (Sp.)—Woven saddle bags.

ALMILLIA (Sp.)—Man's shirt or woman's dress, usually tailored from loom widths of yardage called *bayeta*.

AWAYO (Aym.)—Square cloth worn around a woman's shoulders; carrying cloth used by men and women. (Same as *lliclla*.)

BAYETA (Sp.)—Yardage, handspun and woven on a treadle loom, usually used for making pants, shirts and dresses.

CAITO (Que.)—Handspun yarn.

CAMISA (Sp.)—Shirt.

CAPACHO (Sp.)—Bag with a shoulder strap used to carry food and other goods.

CHALECO (Sp.)—Man's vest.

CHALINA (Sp.)—Woven sash wrapped around the waist; scarf; woman's shawl.

CHULLO (Que.)—Conical knitted cap with earflaps worn by men. (Same as *llucho*.)

CHUMPI (Que.)—Woven belt.

CH'USPA (Que.)—Small woven bag used to carry coca leaves.

COCA (Que. & Aym.)—The plant, *Erythroxylon coca*, E. The leaves of the plant are chewed daily, along with an ash catalyst, by nearly all Bolivian Indians. The leaves help to reduce hunger and alleviate fatigue. They are also used medicinally and for divination. Coca leaves play important roles during all festivals and ceremonies. On a daily basis, coca is always offered upon meeting a friend, when entering any Indian's home, and when receiving guests.

COMPLEMENTARY WARP WEAVE—Technique involving the use of two or more sets of warp threads, usually of different colors, having the same sequence of interlacing but each set interlacing opposite to the other. This is one of the most common techniques used in Bolivia to obtain design patterning.

COSTAL (Sp.)—Woven sack for storing and carrying foodstuffs.

DERIVED WARP WEAVE—Technique in which patterns are formed by skipping the regular interlacings of a plain weave fabric. One or more colors may be used.

DOUBLE CLOTH WEAVE—Technique involving the use of two complete sets of warp which are woven simultaneously resulting in two interconnected layers of fabric.

HONDA (Sp.)—Sling, used for herding; in ancient times, a weapon to hurl rocks.

IKAT (Malay)—A resist dye technique whereby warp or weft yarns are tightly wrapped at intervals to produce a predetermined pattern when the yarn is dyed and woven.

INCUÑA (Aym.)—Small square cloth used to carry coca leaves or food. (Same as *tari*.)

INTI (Que.)—The sun; a diamond-shaped motif representing the sun, commonly used in Bolivian weaving.

IRA (Puquina)—Long white tunic, sewn up the sides. It is used by the Urus as an overgarment while hunting and fishing.

LLACOYA (Que.)—Rectangular handwoven cloth worn over a man's shoulders.

LLICLLA (Que.)—Square handwoven cloth worn over a woman's shoulders; carrying cloth. (Same as awayo.)

LLOQ'E (Que.)—Yarn spun to the left or with the left hand; Z-twisted yarn.

LLUCHU (Aym.)—Conical knitted cap with earflaps, worn by men. (Same as chullo.)

OJOTAS (Sp.)—Sandals used by men and women.

PICHI (Aym.)—Metal pin of gold, silver or copper, used to fasten a woman's awayo or lliclla. (Same as topo.)

POLLERA (Sp.)—Full pleated skirt worn by modern Aymara and mestizo women.

PONCHITO (Sp.)—Small poncho.

PONCHO (Sp.)—Cape-like overgarment worn by men, consisting of two pieces of handloomed cloth sewn together lengthwise with a slit for the head.

PUSHKA (Que.)—Drop spindle.

P'ANTA (Que. & Aym.)—Woman's headcloth which hangs from the back of the head.

REBOZO (Sp.)—Woman's shawl, of Spanish origin, usually made of embroidered felt and used in conjunction with a lliclla or an awayo.

SUPPLEMENTARY WEAVE—Technique involving the use of extra warp or weft threads which are decorative and not essential to the structure of the fabric.

TARI (Aym.)—Small cloth used to carry coca leaves or food. (Same as Incuña.)

TESNU (Aym.)—A woven or braided piece used as a belt tie.

TOPO (Que.)—Metal pin of silver, gold or copper used to fasten a woman's lliclla or awayo. (Same as Pichi.)

TULMA (Que.)—Man's or woman's hairtie.

UNKU (Que.)—Tunic-like shirt; in some regions unku refers to a small cloth worn on the back or a ponchito.

URKU (Aym.)—Full skirt gathered at the waist.

WAKA (Aym.)—Woven belt.

WATADO (Que.)—Warp ikat technique; derived from the Quechua word watay, to tie or wrap.

WAYAKA (Que.)—Small handwoven bag used to carry coca leaves and foodstuffs.

WICHI-WICHI (Aym.)—Ceremonial pompons used in Aymara festivals.

WINCHA (Que.)—Woven headband adorned with glass beads, worn by the women of Charazani.

## FOOTNOTES

1. Collasuyo was the largest and southernmost quarter of the Inca empire. Its inhabitants were called *Collas*.

2. Weston La Barre, "The Aymara Indians Of the Lake Titicaca Plateau, Bolivia," *American Anthropologist,* vol. 50, no. 1, part 2 (1948) p. 19.

3. Daniel W. Gade, *Plants, Man and the Land in the Vilcanota Valley of Peru* (The Hague, 1975).

4. For an extensive listing of natural dyes used in the Charazani region, see Louis Girault, *Textiles Boliviens, Region de Charazani* (France, 1969). Also see Weston LaBarre, *op. cit.*

5. Belts are the exception. Several inches of warp are left at the ends of belts to be braided or finger woven.

6. When there are more than two colors, the other color or colors are usually hidden when not being pulled forward as part of the design.

7. For excellent discussions on Bolivian weave structures, techniques and looms, see Ann Pollard Rowe, *Warp-patterned Weaves of the Andes* (Washington, D.C., 1977), and Marjorie Cason and Adele Cahlander, *The Art of Bolivian Highland Weaving* (New York, 1976).

8. Gösta Montell, "Le Vrai Poncho, Son Origine Post-Colombienne," *Journal de la Société de Américanistes de Paris,* Vol. XVII (Paris, 1925).

9. The act of making offerings to *Pachamama* is not restricted to festivals; in fact, it is always done before eating, drinking or chewing coca.

10. The *alforjas* are the trademark of the *Callahuayas*. The name *Callahuaya* actually comes from the Aymara words *q'ola* (medicine), and *wayu* (a kind of bag).

11. Louis Girault, *op. cit.,* p. 45.

12. Joseph William Bastien, *Qollahuaya Rituals: An Ethnographic Account of Man and Land in an Andean Village* (Cornell, 1973).

13. *Ibid.*

14. The type of textiles woven in this area before 1900 is not known.

## BIBLIOGRAPHY

Bastien, Joseph William, *Qollahuaya Rituals: An Ethnographic Account of Man and Land in an Andean Village* (Latin American Studies Program, Dissertation Series, Cornell University, August, 1973).

Cason, Marjorie and Cahlander, Adele, *The Art of Bolivian Highland Weaving* (New York: Watson-Guptill Publications, 1976).

Costas Arguedos, José Felipe, *Diccionario del Folklore Boliviano* (Sucre, Bolivia: Universidad Mayor de San Francisco, 1961).

Crawford, M. D. C., "The Loom in the New World," *American Museum Journal,* vol, 16, no. 6 (1916), pp. 381-388.

Emery, Irene, *The Primary Structures of Fabrics: an Illustrated Classification* (Washington, D.C.: The Textile Museum, 1966).

Forbes, David, "On the Aymara Indians of Bolivia and Perú," *Journal of the Ethnological Society*, no. 2 (London, 1870), pp. 193-305.

Girault, Louis, *Textiles Boliviens, Region de Charazani*, Catalogues du Musée de l'Homme, Series H: Amérique (Paris: Musée National d'Histoire Naturelle, 1969).

Goins, J. F., "The Present Distribution of Indian Languages in Highland Bolivia," *Kroeber Anthropological Society Papers*, no. 2 (Berkeley: 1950), pp. 17-34.

Guamán Poma de Ayala, Felipe, *La Nueva Crónica y Buen Gobierno* (Lima: reprint, Gráfica Industrial, 1966).

Harcourt, Raoul d', *Textiles of Ancient Peru and Their Techniques*; Edited by Grace G. Denny and Caroline M. Osborne; translated by Sadie Brown (Seattle: The University of Washington Press, 1962; paperback, 1974).

La Barre, Weston, "The Aymara Indians of the Lake Titicaca Plateau, Bolivia," *American Anthropologist*, vol. 50, no. 1, part 2, Memoir series, no. 68 (Menasha, Wisc.: January, 1948).

_____, "The Uru-Chipaya" in: *Handbook of the South American Indians*, vol. II (New York: Cooper Square Publishers, Inc., 1963), pp. 575-585.

Lara, Jesús, *Diccionario Quëshwa-Castellano Castellano-Quëshwa* (La Paz: Editorial Los Amigos del Libro, 1971).

Luquet, G. H., "Décor de Ceintures Boliviennes," *Social Science Abstracts*, 3:7, no. 10467 (Berlin, 1930), pp. 93-101.

Miller, L. E., "A Glimpse into the Quichua Country of Southern Bolivia," *American Museum Journal*, vol. XVII, no. 6 (New York, 1917), pp. 407-415.

Montell, Gösta, "Le Vrai Poncho, Son Origine Post-Colombienne," *Journal de la Société de Américanistes de Paris*, Vol. XVII (Paris, 1925).

_____, *Dress and Ornaments in Ancient Peru* (Göteborg, 1929).

Murra, John V., "Cloth and its Function in the Incan State," *American Anthropologist*, vol. 64, no. 4 (Menasha, Wisc.: 1962), pp. 720-738.

O'Neale, Lila M., "Weaving" in: *Handbook of the South American Indians*, vol. V (New York: Cooper Square Publishers, Inc., 1963), pp. 97-137.

Rigoberto Paredes, M., *Trajes y Armas Indígenas* (La Paz: reprint, Ediciones Isla, 1964).

_____, *Vocabulario de la Lengua Aymara* (La Paz: Ediciones Isla, 1971).

Rowe, Ann Pollard, *Warp-Patterned Weaves of the Andes* (Washington, D.C.: The Textile Museum, 1977).

Torrico Prado, Benjamin, *Indígenas en el Corazón de America* (La Paz: Editorial Los Amigos del Libro, 1971).

Tshopik, Harry Jr., "The Aymara," in: *Handbook of the South American Indians*, vol. II (New York: Cooper Square Publishers, Inc., 1963), pp. 501-573.

Zimmern, Nathalie H., *Introduction to Peruvian Costume* (Brooklyn, New York: The Brooklyn Museum, 1949).

*printing:* Typecraft
*typography:* Garon Graphic
*graphic design:* Max King
*photography:* Bob Seida - all textile photography
Laurie Adelson - pp. 7, 24, 43
Bruce Takami - pp. 2, 8, 9, 12, 15, 16, 17,
20, 27, 32, 35, 40, 44, 47, 51, 61
Roger Yorke - pp. 19, 28, 31, 36, 39, 48

Craft & Folk Art Museum • 5814 Wilshire Boulevard • Los Angeles, CA 90036